THE PROSE AND POETRY SERIES

Story

Time

SECOND EDITION

MARJORIE PRATT

MARY MEIGHEN

Revised by Floy Winks DeLancey
Associate Professor of English,
New York State University Teachers College,
Brockport, New York

Illustrations by Carol Critchfield
and Guy Brown Wiser Associates

Design by Stefan Salter

THE L. W. SINGER COMPANY

A Division of Random House, Inc.

Syracuse	Atlanta	Chicago	Dallas	Menlo Park
New York	Georgia	Illinois	Texas	California

Stories and Poems

Little Frisky Goat

Little Frisky Goat lived
with his father and his mother.

They lived on a big farm.

One day Little Frisky Goat ran away
from the farm.

He ran on and on.

He did not know where he was going.

At last he came to the big woods
that was far away.

He went into the woods.

6

Little Frisky Goat went on and on
into the woods.

He stopped to look around.

There were trees all around him.

He did not know where to go.

He did not know how to get
out of the woods.

He was afraid.

A tiger saw Frisky Goat.
"Stop, little goat!" he called.
"I want to eat you."

"No, do not eat me,"
said Frisky Goat.
"I am looking for my mother
and father."

"Go and find your mother and
father," said the tiger.
"I will eat all three of you."

Frisky Goat ran on.
He saw Big Alligator in a pond.

Big Alligator looked at him.
"Stop, little goat!" said Big Alligator.
"I will get out of this pond.
I am going to eat you."

"Do not eat me now, Big Alligator,"
said Frisky Goat.
"I am looking for my mother
and father."

"Go and find your mother and
father," said Big Alligator.
"I want to eat all three of you."

Frisky Goat went on.

He was afraid.

Where was his mother?

Where was his father?

He wanted his mother and his father.

He did not know how to get
out of the woods.

He did not know how to find
his home.

Frisky Goat stopped.
He saw a big lion.

The lion looked at Frisky Goat.
"Little goat," he said,
"I am going to eat you."

"Do not eat me now,"
said Frisky Goat.
"I am looking for my mother
and father."

"Go and find your mother and
father," said the lion.
"I want to eat all three of you."

11

Frisky Goat ran on.

He began to cry.

He wanted his mother and father.

He wanted to get out of the woods.

Big Elephant saw Frisky Goat crying.
"Why are you crying?"
said Big Elephant.

Frisky Goat said, "I want my mother
and my father.

The tiger wants to eat me.

Big Alligator wants to eat me.

The lion wants to eat me.

Do you want to eat me?"

Big Elephant said, "No! No!
I do not want to eat you.
I do not want to eat a little goat.
We will find your mother and
father."

Big Elephant put his trunk
around Frisky Goat.

Away went Big Elephant
and Frisky Goat out of the woods.

On and on went Big Elephant.
On and on went Frisky Goat.

At last Frisky Goat looked up.
"Oh," he said, "there is my farm.
There are my mother and father."
How happy Frisky Goat was
to see them!

Big Elephant put Frisky Goat down.
"Run to your mother and father,"
he said.
"Do not go into the woods again."

Do You Know?

1. Where did Frisky Goat live?

2. Where did Frisky Goat go?

3. Who said, "I will get out of this pond.

I am going to eat you"?

4. Who said, "Little goat, I am going to eat you"?

5. Who said, "No! No!

I do not want to eat a little goat"?

6. Who wanted his mother and father?

Piggity Pig

One day Piggity Pig said,
"Mother, I want to go somewhere.
I want to go by myself."

Mother Pig looked at Piggity Pig.
She said, "You are a little pig.
You are too little to go away
by yourself.
Do not go away."

Piggity Pig said, "I am not
a little pig.
I am a big pig.
I want to go away by myself."

"Piggity Pig" adapted from *The Happy Book* by Josephine Van Dolzen Pease. Copyright, 1942, by Rand McNally & Company, publishers.

16

Mother Pig looked at Piggity Pig.
"You may go," she said.
"I want you to do two things.
Always keep your tail up.
Do not ask questions."

Piggity Pig looked at his mother.
He said, "I will do what you tell me
to do.
I will always keep my tail up.
I will not ask questions."
Piggity Pig put his tail up.
Then away he ran.

Piggity Pig went down the road.
He saw Big Turkey by a tree.
Piggity Pig looked at Big Turkey.
He looked at Big Turkey's
tail feathers.

He asked, "Why do you have
tail feathers?

Why do you keep
your tail feathers up?"

18

Big Turkey looked at Piggity Pig.
"Stop asking questions," he said.
"Go away! Go away!"
Big Turkey ran at Piggity Pig.

Down went Piggity Pig's tail.
Away he went down the road.

Piggity Pig met Billy Goat
in the road.

He looked at Billy Goat.

He looked at Billy Goat's long horns.

"Why do you have horns?"
asked Piggity Pig.

"Why do you have long horns?"

"Why do you ask questions?"
said Billy Goat.

Billy Goat put his head down.

He ran at Piggity Pig.

Away ran Piggity Pig.

His tail went down.

Piggity Pig saw a red cow.
He ran up to the cow.

The cow looked down at Piggity Pig.
"Moo! Moo!" went the cow.

"Oh! Oh!" said Piggity Pig.
"Who are you? Who are you?"

"Moo! Moo!" said the cow.
"Do not ask questions."
The cow ran at Piggity Pig.

Down went Piggity Pig's tail.
Away he ran.

Down the road ran Piggity Pig.
Fast and faster he ran.
"Mother! Mother!" he called.
"I want my mother."
Then Piggity Pig looked up.
He saw someone coming
down the road.
It was Piggity Pig's mother.
Piggity Pig ran to his mother.

His mother looked at him.
"My little pig has his tail down,"
she said.
"You have asked some questions."

Who Am I?

1. My tail feathers were up.

2. I did not want my little pig
to ask questions.

3. I have long horns.

4. I went "Moo! Moo!"

5. I was happy to see my mother.

The Hide-Away Ducks

"Quack! Quack!" said Mother Duck.
"Where are my little ducks?"
Mother Duck ran around the barnyard.
She looked and looked.
She said, "Quack! Quack!
Who knows where my little ducks
are?"

24

"The Hide-Away Ducks" adapted from *The Hide-Away Ducklings* by Jane Flory, published by
Grosset and Dunlap. Copyright, 1946, by Artists and Writers Guild, Inc.

Mother Duck saw Billy Goat.
She ran over to him.
"Oh! Oh! Billy Goat," she said.
"Have you seen my little ducks?"

"No, I have not seen them,"
said Billy Goat.
"Did you look in the garden?"

"No," said Mother Duck.
"I will look there now."
Mother Duck looked
all around the garden.
The little ducks were not there.

Mother Duck saw Red Rooster.
She ran over to him.
"Quack! Quack!" said Mother Duck.
"Have you seen my little ducks?"

"No! No!" said Red Rooster.
"Did you look under the big tree?"

"No," said Mother Duck.
"I will look there now."
Mother Duck looked
under the big tree.
The little ducks were not there.

26

Mother Duck saw two little kittens
playing under the tree.

"Have you seen my little ducks?"
she asked.

"No! No!" said the little kittens.

"We will look for them,"
said one little kitten.

The kittens looked and looked.
They did not find the little ducks.

Mother Duck could not find
the little ducks.

She ran down the road.
She saw White Rabbit.
"Quack! Quack!" said Mother Duck.
"Have you seen my little ducks?"

"No!" said White Rabbit.
"I have not seen the little ducks.
Did you look in the field for them?"

Mother Duck looked in the field.
White Rabbit looked in the field.
They did not find the little ducks.

28

Mother Duck and White Rabbit
ran into the woods.

They saw Gray Squirrel.

"Gray Squirrel," called Mother Duck.
"Have you seen my little ducks?"

"No!" said Gray Squirrel.
"I did not see them."
Gray Squirrel ran up a tree.
He saw some birds.
"Little birds," called Gray Squirrel.
"Have you seen the little ducks?"

"Have you looked in the pond?"
asked the little birds.

Gray Squirrel ran down the tree.
He ran to Mother Duck and
White Rabbit.
"Come!" he said.
"We will go to the pond."

Away ran Mother Duck.
Away ran Gray Squirrel.
Away ran White Rabbit.
They ran to the pond.
They saw the little ducks in the pond.

"Mother!" called the little ducks.
"Look! We know how to swim."

30

Who Am I?

1. I said, "Where are
my little ducks?"

2. I said, "Did you look in the field
for the little ducks?"

3. I said, "Little birds, have you seen
the little ducks?"

4. I said, "Did you look
under the big tree?"

5. I said, "Did you look
in the garden?"

Chicken Little

One day Chicken Little ran
into the garden.
   She wanted to find something to eat.
   She looked under a big tree.
   Whack! Something fell on her tail.

"Oh! Oh!" said Chicken Little.
"The sky is falling!
The sky is falling!
I will run.
I will run to tell the king."
Away ran Chicken Little
to tell the king.
She ran and ran.

Chicken Little met Henny Penny.
"Oh, Henny Penny!"
called Chicken Little.
"The sky is falling!
The sky is falling!"

"How do you know?"
said Henny Penny.

"I saw it with my eyes.
I heard it with my ears.
Some of it fell on my tail,"
said Chicken Little.
"I am going to tell the king."

Henny Penny looked
at Chicken Little.

"I will go with you,"
said Henny Penny.

"We will go to tell the king
that the sky is falling."

Away ran Chicken Little and
Henny Penny to see the king.

On and on they ran down the road.

Chicken Little and Henny Penny
met Cocky Locky.

"Oh, Cocky Locky!"
called Chicken Little.
"The sky is falling!
The sky is falling!"

"How do you know?"
said Cocky Locky.
"How do you know that the sky
is falling?"

"I saw it with my eyes.
I heard it with my ears.
Some of it fell on my tail,"
said Chicken Little.
"We are going to tell the king."

"I will go with you,"
said Cocky Locky.

Chicken Little ran.
Henny Penny and Cocky Locky ran.
They all ran to tell the king.

Chicken Little saw Goosey Poosey
coming down the road.

"Oh, Goosey Poosey!"
called Chicken Little.

"The sky is falling!
The sky is falling!"

"How do you know?"
said Goosey Poosey.

"How do you know that the sky
is falling?"

"I saw it with my eyes.
I heard it with my ears.
Some of it fell on my tail,"
said Chicken Little.

"We are going to tell the king.
Henny Penny is going with me.
Cocky Locky is going with me.
Will you go with me?"

"I will go with you,"
said Goosey Poosey.

Away ran Chicken Little.
Away ran Henny Penny.
Away ran Cocky Locky.
Away ran Goosey Poosey.
They all ran to tell the king
that the sky was falling.

Chicken Little and Henny Penny
went on down the road.

Cocky Locky and Goosey Poosey
went on down the road.

They met Turkey Lurkey.

"Where are you all going?"
said Turkey Lurkey.

"Oh, Turkey Lurkey,"
said Chicken Little.

"The sky is falling!
The sky is falling!"

Turkey Lurkey looked
at Chicken Little.

"How do you know that the sky
is falling?" said Turkey Lurkey.

"I saw it with my eyes.
I heard it with my ears.
Some of it fell on my tail,"
said Chicken Little.

"We are going to tell the king."

Turkey Lurkey looked
at Goosey Poosey.

He looked at Cocky Locky.
He looked at Henny Penny.
Then he looked at Chicken Little.
He said, "No, no, Chicken Little.
The sky is not falling.
We will not go to tell the king.
We will go to the garden.
We will see what fell on your tail."

"I will go to the garden with you,"
said Goosey Poosey.

"I will go with you,"
said Cocky Locky.

"I will go with you,"
said Henny Penny.

Chicken Little said, "I will not go
to the garden.
I know that the sky is falling."

42

"Come, come," said Turkey Lurkey.
"We will all go to the garden."

Turkey Lurkey and Goosey Poosey ran.

Cocky Locky and Henny Penny ran.
Chicken Little ran.
They all ran to the garden.

Turkey Lurkey looked up at the sky.
He looked under a big tree.
He saw something under the tree.
"Oh, Chicken Little,"
said Turkey Lurkey.
"The sky is not falling.
A nut fell on your tail."

Who Are We?

45

Away We Go

Hippity-hop!
Skippity-skop!
We've hopped so long
Our feet won't stop.

We say hello
To those we meet
And hippity-hop
On down the street!

Eleanor Dennis

46

Ferry-Boats

Over the river,
Over the bay,
Ferry-boats travel
Every day.

Most of the people
Crowd to the side
Just to enjoy
Their ferry-boat ride.

Watching the seagulls,
Laughing with friends,
I'm always sorry
When the ride ends.

James S. Tippett

The Gingerbread Boy

Once there was a little old man
and a little old woman.

They lived in a little old house.

One day the little old woman
was baking gingerbread.

She cut out a gingerbread boy
and put it in the oven to bake.

When she opened the oven,
the little gingerbread boy
jumped out.

He ran away.

He ran as fast as he could go.

The little old woman called
to the little old man.
"We must catch
the little gingerbread boy."

So the little old man and
the little old woman ran
after the gingerbread boy.
But they could not catch him.

Soon the gingerbread boy
came to a barn.

He said to the farmer
in the barn, "I ran
from a little old woman.
I ran from a little old man.
And I can run away from you.
I can, I can!"

The farmer ran after the boy.
But he could not catch
the little gingerbread boy.

The gingerbread boy ran on.
He met a man working
in a field.
"I ran from a little old woman.
I ran from a little old man.
I ran away from a farmer.
And I can run away from you.
I can, I can!"

The man in the field ran
after the gingerbread boy.
But he could not catch him.

The boy ran on until he came
to a cow.

He said to the cow,
"I ran from a little old woman,
a little old man, a farmer,
a man in a field.

And I can run away from you.
I can, I can!"

The cow ran after the boy.
But she could not catch him.

Then the gingerbread boy saw
a pig on the road.

He said to the pig,
"I ran from a little old woman,
a little old man, a farmer,
a man in a field, a cow.

And I can run away from you.
I can, I can!"

The pig could not catch the boy.

The gingerbread boy laughed,
and ran on.

A fox jumped into the road.

The boy looked at the fox
and said,
"I ran from a little old woman,
a little old man, a farmer,
a man in a field, a cow,
and a pig.

And I can run away from you.
I can, I can!"

Then the fox began to run.

Now a fox can run very fast.
He ran so fast he caught
the gingerbread boy.
   The fox began to eat the boy.

"Oh, oh, oh!" said
the gingerbread boy.
   "I am half gone!"
   Soon he said, "I am
almost all gone!"
   And then he said,
"I am all gone!"

   That was the end
of the gingerbread boy.

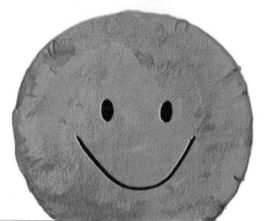

Do You Know?

1. Who made the Gingerbread Boy?
2. Who said, "I can run away from you, I can"?
3. Who ran after the Gingerbread Boy?
4. Who caught the Gingerbread Boy?
5. What happened to the Gingerbread Boy?

The Turnip

A little old man had a garden.
One day he saw a big turnip
in his garden.

"What a big, big turnip," he said.
"I will pull it up."

The little old man tugged
at the turnip.

He could not pull it up.
He tugged and tugged.
He could not pull it up.

The old man called
to the little old woman.

"Help me! Help me!" he said,
"Help me pull up this turnip."

The old man tugged and tugged
at the turnip.

The old woman tugged and tugged
at the old man.

They could not pull up the turnip.

A little girl came by.

The old woman called, "Help! Help! We cannot pull up the turnip."

The little girl ran to help.
The old man tugged at the turnip.
The old woman tugged
at the old man.
The little girl tugged
at the old woman.
They could not pull up the turnip.

"My dog will help,"
said the little girl.
She called her dog.

The old man tugged at the turnip.
The old woman tugged
at the old man.
The little girl tugged
at the old woman.
The dog tugged at the little girl.
They could not pull up the turnip.

The old woman called her cat.

The cat ran into the garden.

The old man tugged at the turnip.

The old woman tugged
at the old man.

The little girl tugged
at the old woman.

The dog tugged at the little girl.

The cat tugged at the dog.

They could not pull up the turnip.

"We cannot pull up the turnip,"
said the old woman.

"We cannot pull up the turnip,"
said the little girl.

"What can we do?" said the old man.
"We cannot pull up the turnip."

"I can help you,"
called a little mouse.
The little mouse ran to help them.

"Pull! Pull!" called the old man.

"Pull! Pull!" called the old woman.

"Pull! Pull!" called the little mouse.

They all gave one big pull,
and up came the turnip.

Who Am I?

1. I helped to pull up the turnip.
   I tugged at the old man.
   I tugged and tugged.
   The little girl tugged at me.
   Who am I?

2. The little girl called me.
   I ran into the garden.
   I helped to pull up the turnip.
   I tugged at the little girl.
   The cat tugged at me.
   Who am I?

63

The Hare and the Tortoise

Once there was a hare.
He was a pretty gray rabbit.
But he was very proud.

Once there was a tortoise.
He was a big brown tortoise.
And he was very kind.

The rabbit made fun of the tortoise.
"What a slow way you have
of going places," he said.
"I do not see how you ever
get where you are going."

"I may be slow," the tortoise
said, "but I always get
where I am going.
I can win a race with you.
Slow as I am, I can win."

The hare laughed.

"I will win," said the hare.
"But if you want to race,
I will race with you."

"Let us ask Mr. Owl
to help us," said the tortoise.
"He can tell who wins.
Mr. Owl is very wise."

So Mr. Owl told them
where to start the race.
He told them to start
at the big tree.
He told them to run to the foot
of the high, high hill.
The first one to get to the foot
of the high, high hill would win.

At first the hare ran very fast.
Then he said, "That tortoise
is so slow.
I can win.
I will stop and rest."

The tortoise slowly walked on.
He did not stop and rest.
At last he came to the foot
of the high, high hill.

By and by the hare woke up.
The sky was dark.
"Oh my, oh my," said the hare.
Then he ran as fast as he could
to the foot of the high, high hill.

There sat the tortoise.
And there sat Mr. Owl.

"Tortoise won the race,"
said Mr. Owl.
"Tortoise walked on and on
to the high, high hill.
The way to win, my friend,
is to keep going."

Let's Make a Play

You can make a play
from "The Hare and the Tortoise."

How many children will be
in the play?
Who will be the hare?
The tortoise? Mr. Owl?

First, act the play
without words.
How will the hare move?
How will the tortoise move?
What will Mr. Owl do?

Now act the play with words.
What will the hare say?
What will the tortoise say?
What will Mr. Owl say?

The Frog on a Log

There once was a green
  Little frog, frog, frog
Who played in the wood
  On a log, log, log.

A screech owl sitting
  In a tree, tree, tree
Came after the frog
  With a scree, scree, scree.

When the frog heard the owl
  In a flash, flash, flash
He leaped in the pond
  With a splash, splash, splash.

Ilo Orleans

"The Frog on a Log" by Ilo Orleans. Reprinted by permission of the author.

69

Not Enough Leather

One day a cat caught a little mouse.
"I will eat you," said the cat.

"Do not eat me," said the mouse.
"Do not eat me.
I will do something for you."

"Not Enough Leather" from "The Mouse Who Turned Tailor" from *Tales from a Finnish Tupa* by James Cloyd Bowman and Margery Bianco. Reprinted by permission of Albert Whitman & Company.

"What can you do?" said the cat.

"I can make a coat for you,"
said the mouse.

"Make a coat for me," said the cat.
"Make a leather coat
and I will not eat you now."
The cat gave the mouse some leather.

Then away ran the mouse
to his home.

The next day the cat came
to get his coat.

"Where is my coat?" he said.

"There was not enough leather
for a coat," said the mouse.

"I will eat you," said the cat.

"Do not eat me," said the mouse.
"I will make a pair of shoes for you.
I have enough leather for a pair
of shoes."

"No, no!" said the cat.
"I will eat you now."

"I can make fine shoes,"
said the mouse.

"Then make a pair of shoes,"
said the cat.

Away ran the mouse.

72

The next day the cat came
to get his shoes.

"Where are my shoes?" he called.

"There was not enough leather
for shoes," said the mouse.

"You did not have enough leather
for a coat," said the cat.

"Now you do not have enough leather
for shoes."

The cat jumped up and down.

"I will eat you now," he said.

"You cannot get away again."

"Do not eat me," said the mouse.
"I will make a cap for you.
I have enough leather for a cap."

"A cap!" said the cat.
"A leather cap!
Then make a cap for me.
I will not eat you now."

74

The next day the cat came
to get his cap.

"Where is my cap?" said the cat.

"There was not enough leather
for a cap," said the mouse.

"Where is my leather that I gave
to you?" said the cat.

"You did not have enough leather
for a coat.

You did not have enough leather
for a pair of shoes.

Now you cannot make a cap.

I will eat you."

"Do not eat me," said the mouse.

"I can make a bag for you.

I have enough leather to make
a beautiful bag."

"Make a bag for me," said the cat.

"I want a beautiful bag.

I will come to see you again."

The next day the mouse said,
"The cat will come to get his bag soon.

I do not know how to make a bag.

I will get out of this house.

I will run away.

That cat will not get into my house again."

The next day the cat wanted
to get his bag.

He went to see the mouse.

He walked up to the door.

He saw something on the door.

He looked at it.

This is what he saw.

Mr. Cat —
I am very
sorry there was
not enough leather
for a bag. You will
never see me again.
Mr. Mouse

The Cat or the Mouse?

1. Who said, "I will eat you"?

2. Who said, "I can make a coat for you"?

3. Who said, "Where is my coat"?

4. Who said, "I will eat you now"?

5. Who said, "There was not enough leather for shoes"?

6. Who said, "You cannot get away again"?

7. Who said, "Then make a cap for me"?

mouse   cat

Who Was the King?

A big whale lived in the water.

He was a very big whale.

"I am the biggest whale
in the water," he said.

"I am the biggest whale in the world.

I am the king of all the world."

"Who Was the King?" adapted from "The Whale and the Elephant" from *Story Book Tales* by Mina Pearl Ashton. Reprinted by permission of Beckley-Cardy Company.

One day the whale looked
out of the water.

He saw a big elephant.

The whale looked at the elephant.

He looked at the elephant's big head.

He looked at the elephant's big feet.

He said, "Who are you?"

The elephant said, "I am
the biggest elephant in the world.

I am the king of the world."

"No, no!" said the whale.
"You are not the king of the world.
I am the king of the world.
You are very, very big.
You may help me to be the king
of the world."

A little rabbit lived in the woods.
He heard what the whale said.
He heard what the elephant said.
The rabbit said, "The elephant is
the king of all the world.
The whale is the king
of all the world.
I will find out who is the king
of the world."

The next day the rabbit said,
"I will see who is the king."

He ran to the water with a big rope.

"Will you help me?" he called
to the whale.

"My cow fell into the mud.
I cannot pull her out."

The whale said, "I am
the biggest whale in the world.

I am king of the world.

I can pull your cow out of the mud."

The little rabbit said, "Come here.
I will tie one end of the rope
to your tail.
I will tie the other end of the rope
to my cow.
You pull the rope when you hear
my drum."
Away ran the little rabbit
to get his drum.

The little rabbit ran to the elephant.
"Will you help me?" he called.
"My cow fell into the mud.
I cannot pull her out."

"I am the biggest elephant
in the world," said the elephant.
"I am the king of the world.
I can pull your cow out of the mud."

The little rabbit said,
"I will tie one end of the rope
to your head.

I will tie the other end of the rope
to my cow.

You pull the rope when you hear
my drum."

Away ran the rabbit.

The elephant heard the drum.
He pulled and pulled the rope.

The whale heard the drum.
He pulled and pulled the rope.

88

The whale put his tail
down into the water.

He pulled and pulled.

The elephant put his head down.
He pulled and pulled.

"What a big cow," said the whale.
He pulled and pulled.

"What a big cow," said the elephant.
He pulled and pulled.

The big rope broke.

Over fell the elephant
on some little trees.

Down went the whale into the water.

The little rabbit ran away.

He did not find out who was the king
of the world.

Do you know?

90

Who Did It?

1. I played a trick on the elephant and the whale.

2. The rabbit tied a rope to my tail.

3. I ran to get my drum.

4. I fell on the little trees.

5. Down I went into the water.

6. I put my head down and pulled and pulled.

Trick or Treat for Sly Old Fox

Sly Old Fox was very hungry.
"I must find some food,"
he said to his friend, Sly Fly.
"I am very hungry.
I will go to the barnyard
and find a treat."
So Sly Old Fox went
to the barnyard.
He saw two fat ducks.
He saw a big fat turkey
and three big chickens.

"What a treat they will be,"
said Sly Old Fox.
"I can catch all of them.
What a treat."
Sly Old Fox walked up to them.
"Good morning, Pretty Ducks,"
he said.
"Good morning, Big Turkey.
Good morning, Red Chickens."

The ducks and the turkey
and the chickens were afraid.
They knew that Sly Old Fox
was not a friend.

"Have you come to eat us?"
asked the two ducks.

"Please do not eat us,"
said the three red chickens.

"Let's go back to the barn,"
said the big turkey.

But Sly Old Fox laughed.
"Oh, you cannot go back
to the barn.
I am going to eat you."

Then the turkey said,
"Let us do one thing before you
eat us.

Let us say good-by."

"Please," said the ducks.
"Let us say good-by."

"Let us do this one thing,"
said the red chickens.
"Then you can eat us.
But let us say good-by."

"That is fair," said the fox.
"Say good-by.
I will sit here and wait."

So the turkey began to talk
very loudly, "Gobble, gobble, gobble."

And the ducks began to talk
very loudly, "Quack, quack, quack."

And the chickens said,
"Cluck, cluck, cluck," as loud as
they could.

Sly Old Fox put his paws
over his ears.
"You are very loud," he said.
"You are very, VERY loud."

Then the two ducks and
the big turkey and the three chickens
began to talk louder and louder.

"QUACK, QUACK, QUACK!"

"GOBBLE, GOBBLE, GOBBLE!"

"CLUCK, CLUCK, CLUCK!"

They talked so loudly
that the farmer heard them.

"What has happened
to my two ducks and
my big turkey and
my three red chickens?"
he said to himself.

And he ran to the barnyard
as fast as he could go.

Sly Old Fox saw the farmer
running over the field.

He jumped up.

"There goes my treat,"
he said.

"Oh, why didn't I eat you
at once."

And Sly Old Fox ran back
to his friend, Sly Fly.

"Where is your food?"
asked Sly Fly.

"Where is that good treat?"

Sly Old Fox began to cry.

"They played a trick on me,"
he said.

"The ducks and the turkey
and the chickens played a trick
on me."

Sly Fly laughed.
"Trick or treat," he said.
"Trick or treat."

Now which was it—
TRICK or TREAT?

Think It Over

1. Mr. Fox wanted something good to eat.

How was he going to get it?

2. The chickens and the ducks did not want Mr. Fox to eat them.

What did they do?

3. Mr. Fox had to run away.

Why did he have to run?

4. Mr. Fox said something to Sly Fly.

What did he say to Sly Fly?

5. Who got a trick and not a treat?

6. When do YOU say "Trick or Treat"?

Wise Johnny

Little Johnny-jump-up said,
"It must be spring,
I just saw a lady-bug
And heard a robin sing."

Edwina Fallis

Down! Down!

Down! Down!
Yellow and brown
The leaves are falling over the town.

Eleanor Farjeon

101

The Queer Company

Long, long ago
there was a little old woman.
She lived in a little house.
All day she spun, spun, spun.
The little old woman wanted company.
No company came to see her.
Still she sat.
Still she spun.
Still she wished for company.

One day the little old woman
heard someone at the door.

A pair of little shoes came in.
The shoes stopped by the chair.

The little old woman looked up.
"Oh, my! Oh, my!" she said.
Still she sat.
Still she spun.
Still she wished for company.

The little old woman
heard someone at the door again.
A pair of little legs came in.
The pair of little legs
jumped into the shoes.

"Oh, oh, what do I see!"
said the little old woman.
Still she sat.
Still she spun.
Still she wished for company.

104

The little old woman
heard someone at the door again.
A big body came in.
The big body sat down
on the pair of little legs.

"Very queer, very queer,"
said the little old woman.
Still she sat.
Still she spun.
Still she wished for company.

The little old woman
heard someone at the door again.
A pair of long arms came in.
They sat down on the big body.

"Very queer, very queer,"
said the little old woman.
Still she sat.
Still she spun.
Still she wished for company.

The little old woman
heard someone at the door again.
A little head came in.
The little head sat down
on the big body.

The little old woman looked up.
She looked at her queer company.

The old woman looked and looked
at her queer company.

She looked at his little shoes.

She said,

"Why do you have little shoes?"

"I run, run, run,"
said the queer company.

"Why do you have little legs?"
said the little old woman.

"I hop, hop, hop,"
said the queer company.

"Where did you get the big body?"
said the little old woman.

"Nobody knows, nobody knows,"
said the queer company.

"Why do you have long arms?"
said the little old woman.

"I paint the sky. I paint the sky,"
said the queer company.

"Where did you get the little head?"
said the little old woman.

"It is a drum,"
said the queer company.

The little old woman said,
"Why did you come to my house?"

"I wanted you to have company,"
said the queer company.

The little old woman still sat
and still spun.
She spun and spun and spun.
She did not wish for company again.

Can You Tell?

1. Where did you get the little head?
2. Why do you have long arms?
3. Why do you have little shoes?
4. Why do you have little legs?
5. Where did you get the big body?
6. Why did you come to my house?

a. Nobody knows.
b. I run, run, run.
c. I paint the sky.
d. I hop, hop, hop.
e. It is a drum.
f. I wanted you to have company.

The Fox at the Spring

Long ago the animals
could not find water to drink.
They looked all over the woods.
They did not know where to go
to find water.

One day one of the bears
saw a spring in the woods.

He called to all the animals,
"Come, come!"

The animals ran to the spring.
They saw the water.
"We can all have a drink," they said.
"We can dig a hole.
The water in the spring will run
into the hole.
We will have all the water
that we can drink."

"We will help to dig a hole,"
said all the rabbits.

"We will help," said all the bears.

"I will help," said a big turtle.

The fox did not want to help.
He ran away.

The animals made a hole.
The water in the spring
ran into the hole.
The animals had all the water
that they could drink.

One day the fox came to the hole
to get a drink.
The animals stopped him.
They said, "You cannot have a drink.
You did not help to dig the hole.
Go away! Go away!"

The next day the fox came
to the hole again to get a drink.
The animals did not let him
get a drink.

"What can we do?" said the bear.
"The fox will come again
when we go away.
Who will sit by the spring to see
that the fox will not get a drink?"

"I will sit by the spring,"
said a big rabbit.

"I will not let the fox get a drink."

The big rabbit sat by the spring.

He sat and sat all day long.

The fox did not come.

The next day the fox came
to get a drink.

He saw the big rabbit.

The rabbit said,
"You cannot have a drink."

"I do not want a drink,"
said the fox.

"I have something that you will want.
I have some honey in my bag."

The fox ate some of the honey.

The rabbit looked at the fox.
"May I have some honey?" he said.

"Yes, yes," said the fox.
"I will give you some honey.
I will tie your legs.
Then I will give you some honey."

"Tie my legs," said the rabbit.
"I want some honey."

"Now I will have a drink,"
said the fox.

"Stop! Stop!" called the rabbit.

The fox did not stop.
He ran to the spring.
He had all the water
that he could drink.
Then he ran away.

"Help! Help!" called the rabbit.

The animals ran to the spring.
They saw the rabbit.
He could not get up.

The turtle looked at the rabbit.
"Did the fox come again?" he said.

"Yes," said the big rabbit.
"The fox did come.
He had all the water
that he could drink."

"What can we do now?"
said one of the bears.

"I will sit by the spring,"
said the turtle.
"I will not let the fox get a drink."
The turtle sat by the spring.

The fox came to get a drink.
He said, "Mr. Turtle, I have
something to eat in my bag."

The turtle heard the fox.
He said nothing.

"I have some honey," said the fox.

The turtle said nothing.

"Do you want some honey?"
said the fox.

The turtle said nothing.

The fox said, "I came to get
some water.
You cannot stop me."
He ran to get a drink.

The turtle caught the fox
by one leg.

The fox could not get away.
"Let me go!" called the fox.
"Let me go! Let me go!
I will give you all of my honey."

The turtle did not let the fox go.

The fox pulled and pulled.
He could not get away.

The animals came to the spring
to get a drink.
The animals jumped on the fox.
They pulled the fox's ears.
They pulled the fox's tail.
They pulled and pulled.

"Oh! let me go," called the fox.
"I will not come to the spring again."

The animals let the fox go.
He did not come to the spring again.

Who?

1. Who called the animals to look at the spring?

2. Who said, "Tie my legs"?

3. Who did not help to dig the hole?

4. Who said, "I want some honey"?

5. Who caught the fox by one leg?

6. Who said, "I will not come to the spring again"?

Little White Rabbit's Trick

Little White Rabbit lived by himself.
He lived by a big pond.
Every day Little White Rabbit
hopped around in the woods.
He was looking for other rabbits.
Every day Little White Rabbit
looked across the pond.
He said to himself, "Are there rabbits
over there?
Do they hop around in the woods?
I wish I could go over there."

126

One day Little White Rabbit
hopped down to the pond.

He saw a crocodile in the water.

He said to himself, "I wish
I could swim.

I wish that I could swim
to the other side of the pond.

What can I do?

How can I get over there?"

The next day Little White Rabbit saw the big crocodile again.

He said to himself, "That crocodile could take me across the pond.

He could take me on his back.

I will play a trick on him.

He will not know that I want to get to the other side of the pond."

Little White Rabbit called, "Hi! Mr. Crocodile."

The crocodile came out of the water. He looked at Little White Rabbit.

The crocodile said, "Why do you
live here by yourself?

There are no rabbits on this side
of the pond.

You have no friends here.

Why do you live here?"

Little White Rabbit said,
"I have no friends here.

I wish that I had some friends.

Mr. Crocodile, you live
in the water.

Do you have friends
in the water?"

The crocodile said,
"All the crocodiles in the pond
are my friends.

I will line them up in the water.

Then you can see them.

I have enough friends to make
a bridge across the pond."

Little White Rabbit said,
"Line up your friends.

Ask them to make a bridge
across the pond.

I want to see how many friends
you have."

The crocodile went down
into the water.

He called all the crocodiles.

They came up out of the water.

Then they made one long line
across the pond.

Little White Rabbit looked
at all the crocodiles.

He said, "Mr. Crocodile,
you do have friends.

I would like to find out
how many friends you have.

I will hop on the back
of each crocodile.

Then I will know how many friends
you have."

Little White Rabbit hopped
on the back of each crocodile.

Soon he was on the other side
of the pond.

Little White Rabbit looked
at Mr. Crocodile in the water.

"Hi, Mr. Crocodile," he called.

"I played a trick on you.

I wanted to get to this side
of the pond.

Your friends made a bridge for me."

Do You Know?

1. Where did Little White Rabbit live?

2. What did Little White Rabbit see in the water?

3. How did Mr. Crocodile show Little White Rabbit how many friends he had?

4. How did Little White Rabbit get across the pond?

The Little Old Woman's Christmas Tree

A Little Old Woman lived in a house near the woods.

She had a big goose called Tilly.

She had a little goose called Floppy.

One morning the Little Old Woman said, "Christmas will soon be here.

I will go into the woods to look for a Christmas tree.

Tilly and Floppy will like a Christmas tree."

134

"The Little Old Woman's Christmas Tree" adapted from "How She Put Up Her Christmas Tree" from *More About the Little Old Woman Who Used Her Head* by Hope Newell. By permission of the publishers, Thomas Nelson & Sons.

The Little Old Woman put on
her coat.

She put an old red hat on her head.

She said, "I will take my hatchet
with me.

I want to chop down a Christmas
tree."

Then the Little Old Woman walked
into the woods.

She walked on and on.

She wanted to see all
of the Christmas trees in the woods.

The Little Old Woman did not know
which Christmas tree to take.

She said, "I want a tall tree.

Tilly and Floppy will like a tall tree."

At last the Little Old Woman saw
a beautiful tall Christmas tree.

She said, "This is the tree
that I will take."

Chop! Chop! Chop! went
the Little Old Woman's hatchet.

Down fell the tall tree.

The Little Old Woman pulled the tree
out of the woods.

She pulled the tree to the door
of her house.

Tilly and Floppy saw
the Little Old Woman with the tree.
They looked at the Christmas tree.
"Hiss! Hiss! Hiss!" they called.

The Little Old Woman said,
"Stop that! Stop that!
You will like this tree when you see it
in the house."

137

The Little Old Woman pulled the tree
into the house.

She could not put the tree up.

It was too tall for her house.

"What will I do?"
said the Little Old Woman.

"I could chop the top off the tree.

No, I will not do that.

A Christmas tree would not be
beautiful if it did not have a top."

138

The Little Old Woman looked around.
She said, "I will sit down
in my chair.
I will use my head.
Then I will know what to do
with that Christmas tree."
The Little Old Woman sat down
in her chair.
She used her head for a long time.
Then the Little Old Woman
jumped up.
She said, "Now I know what I will do.
I will chop a hole in the floor.
Then I will put the tree in the hole."

139

The Little Old Woman chopped
a hole in the floor.

She put the tree in the hole.

The tree was still too tall
for the house.

The Little Old Woman said,
"What will I do now?"

She sat down in her chair.

She said, "I will use my head again."

Soon the Little Old Woman jumped up.

"Now I know what to do," she said.

"I will chop a hole in the roof.

The top of the tree will stick out
of the hole in the roof.

Then I can put the tree up
in my house."

The Little Old Woman climbed up
on the roof of her house.

She chopped and chopped.

Soon there was a hole in the roof.

The Little Old Woman went back
into the house.

She put the Christmas tree in the hole
in the floor.

Then she put the top of the tree
into the hole in the roof.

The Little Old Woman looked
at the tall tree.

"What a beautiful tree this is!"
she said.

"I will call Tilly and Floppy.

How happy they will be to see
this Christmas tree."

Do You Know?

1. Who was the big goose?

2. Who was the little goose?

3. How did the Little Old Woman chop down the Christmas tree?

4. What did Tilly and Floppy call when they saw the Christmas tree?

5. How did the Little Old Woman put up her Christmas tree?

6. What did the Little Old Woman put on her head?

7. Did the Little Old Woman want a tall tree or a little tree?

8. Do you think Tilly and Floppy will like the Christmas tree?

Little Black Bug

Little black bug,
Little black bug,
Where have you been?
I've been under the rug,
Said little black bug.
Bug-ug-ug-ug.

Little green fly,
Little green fly,
Where have you been?
I've been way up high,
Said little green fly.
Buzz-z-z-z.

Margaret Wise Brown

From *Another Here and Now Story Book* by Lucy Sprague Mitchell. Copyright, 1937, by E. P. Dutton & Co. Reprinted by permission of the publisher.

The House Cat

The house cat sits
And smiles and sings.
He knows a lot
Of secret things.

Annette Wynne

The Seventh Little Duck

Seven little ducks lived
in a little house with Mother Duck
and Father Duck.

The little house was near a pond.

Six of the little ducks liked to play
in the pond.

One little duck was afraid to go
into the water.

The other ducks would not play
with him.

146

"The Seventh Little Duck" adapted by permission of the publishers from *Seven Diving Ducks* by Margaret Friskey. Copyright, 1940, by David McKay Co., Inc.

One day Mother Duck called
to the little ducks.

She said, "Come, come, little ducks.

I want all of you to go into the water
with me.

I want you to know how to swim."

Mother Duck walked into the water.

Six of the little ducks went
into the water.

The seventh little duck did not go
with his mother.

Mother Duck began to swim.

She said, "Look at me.

Make your little feet go this way
and you will swim.

One—two! One—two! One—two!"

Soon six of the little ducks knew how
to swim.

Father Duck looked
at the six little ducks.
Then Father Duck looked
at the seventh little duck.
Father Duck said, "We do not want
you to live with us if you cannot swim.
Go and live with the chickens.
They live on the other side
of the pond."

The seventh little duck was not happy.
He wanted to know how to swim.

Every day the seventh little duck
went into the water all by himself.

He wanted to swim
like the other ducks.

He would make his little feet go
one—two, one—two.

At last he knew how to swim.

The seventh little duck could swim
all around the pond.

He could swim to the other side
of the pond.

He could swim to the big apple tree
on the other side of the pond.

One morning Mother Duck called
the little ducks to her.

She said, "All of you can swim.

Now it is time for you to know how
to dive.

You must know how to dive
so you can catch fish."

Mother Duck and her little ducks
went into the water.

"Look at me," said Mother Duck.

"I want you all to know how to dive.

This is the way to dive.

You must go down head first
into the water."

Mother Duck went down head first
into the water.

The seven little ducks looked at her.

Soon she came up with a fish.

Six of the little ducks went down
into the water, head first.

They each came up out of the water
with a fish.

After that, the six little ducks
had fish to eat every day.

The seventh little duck was afraid.

He was afraid to put his head down
into the water.

He could not dive.

He could not catch a fish.

One day Father Duck called
to the little ducks.

He said, "Come here."

The little ducks swam over
to Father Duck.

Father Duck said, "Six of you
know how to dive.

One of you cannot dive.

We do not want a duck
that cannot dive to live with us."

The seventh little duck did not look at Father Duck.

He put his head down and began to cry.

Father Duck looked at the little duck.
He said, "You do not know how to dive.

Go to the other side of the pond and live with the chickens.

We do not want you to live with us."

The seventh little duck swam away.

He began to swim to the other side of the pond.

Mother Duck and the six little ducks looked at the seventh little duck.

They all began to cry.

The seventh little duck swam on to the other side of the pond.

Soon the seventh little duck was
near the big apple tree.

Bump! A big red apple fell
on his head.

Down went the little duck, head first
into the water.

Up he came with a fish.

"Look! Look!" called Father Duck.

"Our seventh little duck knows how
to dive."

Do You Know?

1. How many little ducks lived in the little house near the pond?

2. How many of the little ducks were afraid of the water?

3. Who said, "Little duck, go and live with the chickens"?

4. What made the seventh little duck dive?

5. Who helped the little ducks to swim?

6. Who lived on the other side of the pond?

7. What did the little ducks find when they dived into the water?

a. Mother Duck   d. fish   g. seven

b. Father Duck   e. an apple h. water

c. one   f. chickens i. tree

The Story Clock

WORD LIST

Story Time contains a total of 371 different words, of which 165 are new to this book and on or above the first-grade level. Seven of the 165 new words are proper names, and the 33 words on the first-grade level are noted by an asterisk (*). Words with similar elements are grouped together and may be taught at the same time. A black line separates the vocabulary for each story.

6 his*
  from*
  going*
  far*
7 him*
8 tiger
9 alligator
  pond
11 lion
12 cry
    crying
  elephant
13 trunk
14 them*
    again*

16 Piggity
  somewhere
  myself
    yourself
17 things*
  keep
  tail
  ask*
    asked, 18
    asking, 19
  questions
20 long*
  horns
  head*
21 moo

22 coming*

24 hide
  barnyard
25 seen
  garden*
27 playing
28 field
30 swim

32 whack
33 sky
  falling
  king
34 Henny Penny
  eyes
36 Cocky Locky
38 Goosey Poosey
40 Turkey Lurkey
44 nut

48 gingerbread
  once*
  baking
  oven
  opened
49 catch*
50 soon*
51 working
52 until

54 very*
  caught
  half
  gone
  almost
  end
55 made*

56 turnip
  pull
    pulled, 88
  tugged
58 cannot*
62 gave*
63 helped

64 hare
  tortoise
  pretty*
  proud
  slow
    slowly, 66
  places
    race
  ever
  win
65 let
  owl
  wise
  start
  foot

160